Selections From

Juba This
and
Juba That

*A book of rhymes and
songs to sing and play,
stories to tell, and riddles to guess*

by Virginia A. Tashjian

illustrated by Victoria de Larrea

SCHOLASTIC BOOK SERVICES
NEW YORK · TORONTO · LONDON · AUCKLAND · SYDNEY · TOKYO

For My Favorite Storyteller —
My Mother, Zvart Agababian

Text copyright © 1969 by Virginia A. Tashjian. Illustrations copyright © 1969 by Victoria de Larrea. This abridged edition is published by Scholastic Book Services, a division of Scholastic Magazines, Inc., by arrangement with Little, Brown and Company, Inc.

1st printing .... December 1974

Printed in the U. S. A.

CONTENTS

CHANTS

Chants are a very old form of group entertainment. Here are five. Follow the leader's actions carefully, be very dramatic and you will have fun playing them over and over again.

Juba

Juba this and Juba that
Juba killed a yellow cat
Juba up and Juba down
Juba runnin' all around.

The leader first recites the verse and the group repeats it several times. The actions are added one at a time:

FIRST TIME: *repeat verse slowly and very loudly in singsong cadence.*

SECOND TIME: *repeat verse a little faster and a little more softly in a singsong cadence. At the same time clap hands in rhythm.*

THIRD TIME: *repeat verse a little faster and even more softly. Slap both hands on knees and then clap hands together in rhythm.*

FOURTH TIME: *repeat verse very fast in a very soft voice. At the same time, slap hands on knees, clap hands together, clap hands to both cheeks, clap hands together again in rhythm.*

The leader may repeat the chant as many times as the group wishes, making up more actions.

Head and Shoulders, Baby

Players touch both hands to head and shoulders and clap on "one, two three." Other actions are done as suggested in verse. Still others may be added as desired.

Head and shoulders, Baby—one, two, three.
Head and shoulders, Baby—one, two, three.
Head and shoulders, head and shoulders,
Head and shoulders, Baby—one, two, three.

Knee and ankle, Baby—one, two, three.
Knee and ankle, Baby—one, two, three.
Knee and ankle, knee and ankle,
Knee and ankle, Baby—one, two, three.

Touch the ground, Baby—one, two, three.
Touch the ground, Baby—one, two, three.
Touch the ground, touch the ground,
Touch the ground, Baby—one, two, three.

Stand up, sit down, Baby—one, two, three.
Stand up, sit down, Baby—one, two, three.
Stand up, sit down, stand up, sit down,
Stand up, sit down, Baby—one, two, three.

Who Did?

All clap in rhythm as the leader chants the call in a singsong cadence and the children repeat the response.

CALL: Who did?
RESPONSE: *Who did?*
CALL: Who did?
RESPONSE: *Who did?*
ALL: Who did swallow Jo-Jo-Jo-Jo?

Who did?
   Who did?
Who did?
   Who did?
ALL: Who did swallow Jo-Jo-Jo-Jo?

Who did?
   Who did?
Who did?
   Who did?
Who did swallow Jonah?
   Who did swallow Jonah?
ALL: Who did swallow Jonah down?

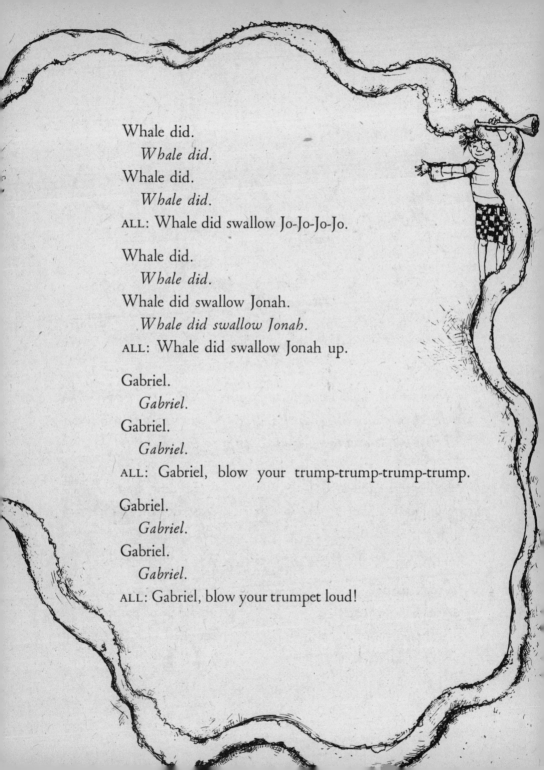

Whale did.
  Whale did.
Whale did.
  Whale did.
ALL: Whale did swallow Jo-Jo-Jo-Jo.

Whale did.
  Whale did.
Whale did swallow Jonah.
  Whale did swallow Jonah.
ALL: Whale did swallow Jonah up.

Gabriel.
  Gabriel.
Gabriel.
  Gabriel.
ALL: Gabriel, blow your trump-trump-trump-trump.

Gabriel.
  Gabriel.
Gabriel.
  Gabriel.
ALL: Gabriel, blow your trumpet loud!

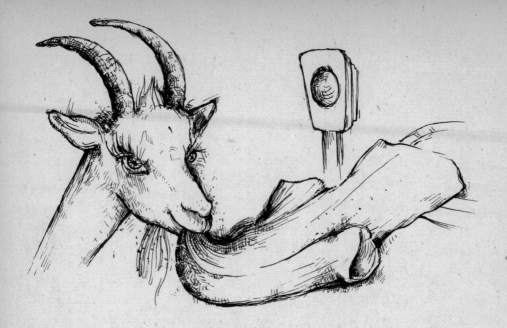

Old Hogan's Goat

Although this may be sung, it is also effective as a chant. The leader chants each line, which is repeated exactly by the children. All clap hands and tap feet in rhythm to the chanting.

Old Hogan's goat
Was feelin' fine,
He ate a red shirt
Right off the line.

I took a stick
And beat his back,
And tied him to
A railroad track.

A speeding train
Was adrawin' nigh,
Old Hogan's goat
Was doomed to die.

He gave an aw-
ful shriek of pain,
Coughed up that shirt
And flagged that train.

The Dark House

The leader chants each line or every half-line in a soft, slow, sepulchral voice. Children repeat each line in the same way. The telling becomes more ghostly and spooky with each line. The last word is a sudden shout!

In a dark, dark wood, there was a dark, dark house,
And in that dark, dark house, there was a dark, dark room,
And in that dark, dark room, there was a dark, dark cupboard,
And in that dark, dark cupboard, there was a dark, dark shelf,
And in that dark, dark shelf, there was a dark, dark box,
And in that dark, dark box, there was a GHOST!

POETRY AND RHYME

Read these poems at different speeds, finishing the rhymes and guessing the subject of some of them. Then make up some lime-ricks of your own to share with your group.

Adventures of Isabel

As the leader recites this, the listeners should repeat the refrain.

Isabel met an enormous bear,
Isabel, Isabel didn't care;
The bear was hungry, the bear was ravenous,
The bear's mouth was cruel and cavernous.
The bear said, Isabel, glad to meet you,
How do, Isabel, now I'll eat you!
Isabel, Isabel, didn't worry,
Isabel didn't scream or scurry.
She washed her hands and she straightened her hair up,
Then Isabel quietly ate the bear up.

Once in a night as black as pitch
Isabel met a wicked witch.
The witch's face was cross and wrinkled,
The witch's gums with teeth were sprinkled.
Ho ho, Isabel! the old witch crowed,
I'll turn you into an ugly toad!
Isabel, Isabel, didn't worry,
Isabel didn't scream or scurry,
She showed no rage and she showed no rancor,
But she turned the witch into milk and drank her.

—*Ogden Nash*

The Toaster

For full enjoyment of this poem, do not reveal the title; read the poem and ask for guesses as to what it's about.

A silver-scaled Dragon with jaws flaming red
Sits at my elbow and toasts my bread.
I hand him fat slices, and then, one by one,
He hands them back when he sees they are done.

—*William Jay Smith*

If You Ever

The leader should recite this alone once. When the children recognize the rhythm, they will chime in.

If you ever ever ever ever ever
    If you ever ever ever meet a whale
You must never never never never never
    You must never never never touch its tail:
For if you ever ever ever ever ever
    If you ever ever ever touch its tail,
You will never never never never never
    You will never never meet another whale.

What Did You Put in Your Pocket?

The audience joins in each refrain.

What did you put in your pocket
What did you put in your pocket
   in your pockety pockety pocket
Early Monday morning?

I put in some chocolate pudding
I put in some chocolate pudding
   slushy glushy pudding
Early Monday morning.

    Refrain: SLUSHY GLUSHY PUDDING!

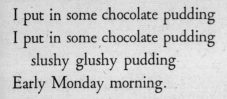

What did you put in your pocket
What did you put in your pocket
   in your pockety pockety pocket
Early Tuesday morning?

I put in some ice-cold water
I put in some ice-cold water
   nicy icy water
Early Tuesday morning.

    Refrain: SLUSHY GLUSHY PUDDING!
           NICY ICY WATER!

What did you put in your pocket
What did you put in your pocket
   in your pockety pockety pocket
Early Wednesday morning?

I put in a scoop of ice cream
I put in a scoop of ice cream
   slurpy glurpy ice cream
Early Wednesday morning.

           Refrain: SLUSHY GLUSHY PUDDING!
                NICY ICY WATER!
                SLURPY GLURPY ICE CREAM!

What did you put in your pocket
What did you put in your pocket
   in your pockety pockety pocket
Early Thursday morning?

I put in some mashed potatoes
I put in some mashed potatoes
   fluppy gluppy potatoes
Early Thursday morning.

Refrain: SLUSHY GLUSHY PUDDING!
NICY ICY WATER!
SLURPY GLURPY ICE CREAM!
FLUPPY GLUPPY POTATOES!

What did you put in your pocket
What did you put in your pocket
in your pockety pockety pocket
Early Friday morning?

I put in some sticky molasses
I put in some sticky molasses
sticky icky molasses
Early Friday morning.

Refrain: SLUSHY GLUSHY PUDDING!
NICY ICY WATER!
SLURPY GLURPY ICE CREAM!
FLUPPY GLUPPY POTATOES!
STICKY ICKY MOLASSES!

What did you put in your pocket
What did you put in your pocket
in your pockety pockety pocket
Early Saturday morning?

I put in my five fingers
I put in my five fingers
   funny finny fingers
Early Saturday morning.

      Refrain: SLUSHY GLUSHY PUDDING!
               NICY ICY WATER!
               SLURPY GLURPY ICE CREAM!
               FLUPPY GLUPPY POTATOES!
               STICKY ICKY MOLASSES!
               FUNNY FINNY FINGERS!

What did you put in your pocket
What did you put in your pocket
   in your pockety pockety pocket
Early Sunday morning?

I put in a clean white handkerchief
I put in a clean white handkerchief
   a spinky spanky handkerchief
Early Sunday morning.

Refrain: SLUSHY GLUSHY PUDDING!

NICY ICY WATER!

SLURPY GLURPY ICE CREAM!

FLUPPY GLUPPY POTATOES!

STICKY ICKY MOLASSES!

FUNNY FINNY FINGERS!

SPINKY SPANKY HANDKERCHIEF!

—*Beatrice Schenk de Regniers*

Fire! Fire!

It's fun to make up different rhyming endings for this familiar verse. The leader may omit the last word of each line and let the listeners supply the rhyme.

"Fire! Fire!"
Cried Mrs. _____ (McGuire)

"Where? Where?"
Cried Mrs. _____ (Blair)

"All over town!"
Cried Mrs. _____ (Brown)

"Get some water!"
Cried Mrs. _____ (Potter)

"We'd better jump!"
Cried Mrs. _____ (Gump)

"That would be silly!"
Cried Mrs. _____ (Brunilly)

"It looks too risky!"
Cried Mrs. _____ (Matriski)

"What'll we do?"
Cried Mrs. _____ (La Rue)

"Turn in an alarm!"
Cried Mrs. _____ (La Farme)

"Save us! Save us!"
Cried Mrs. _____ (Potayvus)

This Man Had Six Eyes

*To make this doubly enjoyable, do not read all of the last line;
give the children time to guess the identity of the "man."*

I met a man that had six eyes
And still he could not see.
He lay in bed and hid his head
And would not look at me.

I pulled him up and took him home
(I don't think I did wrong.)
And I let him stay, and day by day
I saw his eyes grow long.

I saw them grow out of his head.
I saw them turn to me.
I saw them grow a foot or so.
And *still* he could not see.

"I think he could see the sun," I said,
So I put him on the sill,
And gave him a drink. But what do you think?
His eyes kept growing still.

They grew as long as I was tall.
They grew like a sleepy tree.
They grew to the floor and out the door.
And still they could not see.

Now what do you think has eyes that long?
You may tell me now if you know.
Or look in the pot: there, like as not,
You will find . . . MR. POT 8 OH!

—John Ciardi

Poor Old Lady Swallowed a Fly

Although this may also be sung, it is equally effective for a group to recite together. Leader starts; children follow.

Poor old lady, she swallowed a fly.
I don't know why she swallowed a fly.
Poor old lady, I think she'll die.

Poor old lady, she swallowed a spider.
It squirmed and wriggled and turned inside her.
She swallowed the spider to catch the fly.
I don't know why she swallowed a fly.
Poor old lady, I think she'll die.

Poor old lady, she swallowed a bird.
How absurd! She swallowed a bird.
She swallowed the bird to catch the spider,
She swallowed the spider to catch the fly.
I don't know why she swallowed a fly.
Poor old lady, I think she'll die.

Poor old lady, she swallowed a cat.
Think of that! She swallowed a cat.
She swallowed the cat to catch the bird.
She swallowed the bird to catch the spider.
She swallowed the spider to catch the fly.
I don't know why she swallowed a fly.
Poor old lady, I think she'll die.

Poor old lady, she swallowed a dog.
She went the whole hog when she swallowed the dog.
She swallowed the dog to catch the cat,
She swallowed the cat to catch the bird,
She swallowed the bird to catch the spider.
She swallowed the spider to catch the fly,
I don't know why she swallowed a fly.
I think she'll die.

Poor old lady, she swallowed a cow.
I don't know how she swallowed the cow.
She swallowed the cow to catch the dog,
She swallowed the dog to catch the cat,
She swallowed the cat to catch the bird,
She swallowed the bird to catch the spider,
She swallowed the spider to catch the fly,
I don't know why she swallowed a fly.
Poor old lady, I think she'll die.

Poor old lady, she swallowed a horse.
She died, of course.

—*Rose Bonne*

Limericks

There once was a boy of Bagdad,
An inquisitive sort of a lad.
    He said, "I will see
    If a sting has a bee."
And he very soon found that it had!

A flea and a fly in a flue
Were caught, so what could they do:
    Said the fly, "Let us flee."
    "Let us fly," said the flea.
So they flew through a flaw in the flue.

There once was a plesiosaurus
Which lived when the earth was all porous.
But it fainted with shame
When it first heard its name,
And departed long ages before us.

An oyster from Kalamazoo
Confessed he was feeling quite blue,
"For," says he, "as a rule,
When the weather turns cool,
I invariably get in a stew!"

A sleeper from the Amazon
Put nighties of his gra'mazon—
The reason, that
He was too fat
To get his own pajamazon.

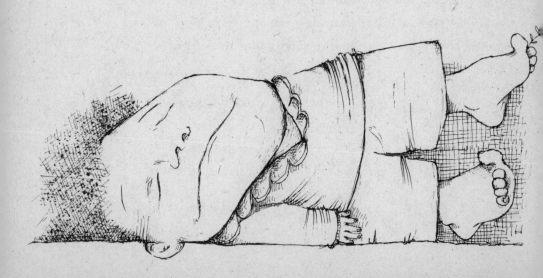

Antonio

Read this once slowly and with exaggerated concern; on second reading, invite the audience to join in, if they do not do so spontaneously.

Antonio, Antonio,
Was tired of living alonio.
 He thought he would woo
 Miss Lissamy Loo
Miss Lissamy Lucy Molonio.

Antonio, Antonio,
Rode off on his polo-polonio.
  He found the fair maid
  In a bowery shade,
A-sitting and knitting alonio.

Antonio, Antonio,
Said, "If you will be my ownio,
  I'll love you true,
  And I'll buy for you,
An icery creamery conio!"

"Oh, Nonio, Antonio! . .
You're far too bleak and bonio!
  And all that I wish,
  You singular fish,
Is that you will quickly begonio."

Antonio, Antonio,
He uttered a dismal moanio;
  Then ran off and hid
  (Or I'm told that he did)
In the Anticatarctical Zonio.

       —*Laura E. Richards*

STORIES

These are all audience-participation and action stories of one kind or another. Some might even be called action games. In order to enjoy them fully, sing out the refrains and repetitions along with the leader. If you read them by yourself, shout them out anyway.

Where the story calls for repeated actions, follow the leader carefully. You will discover how much more fun it is when anyone makes a mistake.

The Busy Farmer's Wife

The leader tells the story and demonstrates the actions. Children imitate the actions. Each motion, once started, is continued after the next one begins so that, by the end of the story, all motions are going on at once.

The farmer's wife has many duties. She keeps busy all day long. The other day I visited a friend of mine and found her in the kitchen. She was standing at the stove stirring a big pot of apple butter.

> *(Make stirring motion with right hand.)*

The churn was standing nearby and she was pumping the handle up and down as she stirred the apple butter.

> *(Make pumping motion up and down with left hand; continue stirring motion with the right hand.)*

One of the girls came in with a piece of taffy she had made at a taffy party, and put a piece in her mother's mouth. So there my friend stood, stirring and pumping the churn and chewing.

(Make chewing motion with mouth
while continuing other motions.)

All of a sudden she noticed that the screen door had been left open and the chickens were coming in the kitchen. She couldn't leave her churning and the apple butter, so all she could do was stand there shaking her head at the chickens and yelling, "Shoo, shoo, shoo."

(Move head up and down as if gesturing
toward the door while making shooing sounds.
Continue all other motions.)

The Lion Hunt

Lion hunting is dangerous; thus, it is necessary to stay together. Group must repeat everything exactly as the leader says it and does it.

LEADER: Do you WANT to go on a lion hunt?
    (Children may answer in various ways. Leader reminds children they must repeat her words and actions exactly.)

CHILDREN: Do you WANT to go on a lion hunt?

LEADER: Well, then, let's go.

CHILDREN: Well, then, let's go.

This pattern of repetition of EVERY line and action continues throughout the whole story.

Let's start walking.
>   (*Make walking sounds with feet on floor.*)

We'll have to cross a bridge.
>   (*Hit palms on thighs to simulate sound of feet on bridge.*)

Now we're across the bridge.

Horses are waiting for us here.

We'll ride part of the way.
>   (*Hold reins in hands. Bounce up and down. Make clucking sounds with tongue to simulate sound of horses hooves on ground. Give occasional "giddap."*)

This is as far as we can go with the horses.

We'll have to walk from here.
>   (*Make walking sounds with feet.*)

Oh! It's beginning to rain.
>   (*Rub palms together in circular motion to make sounds of rain.*)

It's getting muddy.

We'll have to walk in the mud.

It's hard going.
>   (*Make claws of hands, turn palms down and make motions in walking rhythm as if pulling feet in mud. Make juicy, slurpy sound with mouth.*)

In fact, we're walking through a bog.
>   (*Continue slurping sound and same motions.*)

The mosquitoes are biting.
>   (*Slap at face and neck; scratch here and there; continue slurping walk through bog.*)

We're finally on dry ground now.

We can walk a little faster.
>   (*Make walking sounds with feet.*)

Oh, oh, wait a minute.

I think I see something.
>   (*Hold hand to eye.*)

Yes, I see a stream.

Shall we take a run?

And jump over it?

Ready?

Let's go.
>   (*Make running rhythm, slapping palms on thighs. Raise palms in midair, hold for a moment, hit thighs again, simulating sounds of a jump over the stream.*)

42

We made it!

We'll have to walk through the reeds.
> (*Put hands in front of face to separate reeds which block passage.*)

Now we're on clear ground again.
> (*Make walking sounds with hands slapping thighs.*)

Stop!

Wait a minute.

I see a big river.

Let's take a long run.

And a big jump.

If we don't make it, we'll have to swim.

Ready?

Run!
> (*Make running rhythm, slapping palms on thighs. Raise hands and hold in midair for a moment.*)

We'll never make it.

We'll have to swim.
> (*Hold nose with hands as if diving into water. Make spluttering noises. Begin swimming strokes.*)

We can walk the rest of the way.
> (*Make slurping sounds; pretend to walk in slow, painful crawl.*)

Well, we made it to shore.
      (Wring out clothes and hair and shake self.)

It ought to be easier from here on.

Let's go.
      (Make walking rhythm with feet.)

Hold it.
      (Put hand to eyes.)

I see a cave.

Shall we go in?

Careful now, here we go.
      (Cup hands to mouth once inside cave.)

It's dark in here.

I wonder if there's anyone here.

Yoo hoo.
      (Louder.)

I hear an echo.

Yooooooo. Hooooooo.

Hey.

I just happened to think of something.

There may be bears in here.

Let's get out of here.
  (*Make running sounds with feet.*)

Phew.

I'm glad we got out of there safely.

We'll have to climb this hill.
  (*Make slow walking rhythm.*)

It's getting steeper and steeper.

We'll have—to—go—slower—and slower.

Phew.

We're almost to the top.

Just a little farther.
  (*Make footsteps slower and slower.*)

Now we're at the top.

Let's rest a minute.

Take a deep breath.
  (*Take a loud sniff.*)

Isn't the air wonderful?
  (*Hit hands on chest.*)

Makes you feel so good.

Look at the beautiful view.

> (*Put hands to eyes, turning complete circle as though looking around.*)

Everybody rested?

Shall we run down the hill?

Ready?

Get set.

Go!

> (*Make running rhythm with feet on floor.*)

Shhhhhhhhhhhhhhhh.

> (*Put finger to mouth.*)

We're near lion country.

We'll walk through this tall grass.

Grass makes a swishing sound.

> (*Slap palms together in swishing, not clapping sound. Make swishing sound with mouth.*)

Stop.

> (*In whisper.*)

This is where I last saw a lion.

Let's climb a tree.

> (*Curve arms as if climbing tree. Move hands higher and higher.*)

Careful, don't fall, now.

Hold on tight.

Let's look in this direction.

See anything?

I don't see anything.

Let's look in this direction.
     (*Hold tree with one hand, put other hand to eye.*)

See anything?

I don't see anything.

Look over here.

Can you see anything?

I don't see anything.

Now look this way.

Shuuuuuuuuuuush!

I think I see something.

It has two big eyes.

And a long tail.

It's waving back and forth.

Back and forth.

It looks like a lion.

It is a lion.

Hand me the gun.

I don't have the gun.

Do you have the gun?

YOU don't have the gun?

Let's get out of here.
> (*Make motion of sliding down the tree. Whole party retraces steps in a dash, running up the hill, down the hill, and into the cave.*)

Let's wait here.

The lion may not find us.

SHHHHHHHSH.

Now, carefully, let's tiptoe out.
> (*Make motion of tiptoe walking.*)

Now hurry!
> (*Retrace route in double-quick time, swimming the river, walking over hard ground, walking through the reeds, running and jumping the stream, walking over the dry ground, walking through the bog, walking in the mud, walking through the rain sounds, riding horses, walking over the bridge, and so on.*)

We made it.

But if I ever go lion hunting with you again, I'll be sure to take the gun.

You can get killed going hunting without a gun!

The Snooks Family

An audience-participation story. Follow the leader!

ONE NIGHT Mr. and Mrs. Snooks were going to bed as usual. It so happened that Mrs. Snooks got into bed first, and she said to her husband, "Please, Mr. Snooks, would you blow the candle out?"

And Mr. Snooks replied, "Certainly, Mrs. Snooks." Whereupon he picked up the candlestick and began to blow, but unfortunately he could only blow by putting his under lip over his upper lip, which meant that his breath went up to the ceiling instead of blowing out the candle flame.

And he puffed and he puffed and he puffed, but he could not blow it out.

So Mrs. Snooks said, "I will do it, my dear," and she got out of bed and took the candlestick from her husband and began to blow. But unfortunately she could only blow by putting her upper lip over her under lip, so that all her breath went down onto the floor. And she puffed and she puffed, but she could not blow the candle out.

So Mrs. Snooks called their son John. John put on his sky-blue dressing gown and slipped his feet into his primrose-colored slippers and came down into his parents' bedroom.

"John, dear," said Mrs. Snooks, "will you please blow out the candle for us?"

And John said, "Certainly, Mummy."

But unfortunately John could only blow out of the right corner of his mouth, so that all his breath hit the wall of the room instead of the candle.

And he puffed and he puffed, but he could not blow out the candle.

So they all called for his sister, little Ann. And little Ann put on her scarlet dressing gown and slipped on her pink slippers and came down to her parents' bedroom.

"Ann, dear," said Mr. Snooks, "will you please blow the candle out for us?"

And Ann said, "Certainly, Daddy."

But unfortunately Ann could only blow out of the left side of her mouth, so that all her breath hit the wall instead of the candle.

And she puffed and she puffed and she puffed, but she could not blow out the candle.

It was just then that they heard in the street below a heavy, steady tread coming along the pavement. Mr. Snooks threw open

the window and they all craned their heads out. They saw a policeman coming slowly towards the house.

"Oh, Mr. Policeman," said Mrs. Snooks, "will you come up
and blow out our candle? We do so want to go to bed."

"Certainly, Madam," replied the policeman, and he entered
and climbed the stairs—blump, blump, blump. He came into the
bedroom where Mr. Snooks, Mrs. Snooks, John Snooks and little
Ann Snooks were standing around the candle which they could
NOT blow out.

The policeman then picked up the candlestick in a very dignified
manner and, putting his mouth into the usual shape for blowing,
puffed out the candle at the first puff. Just like this—PUFF!

Then the Snooks family all said, "Thank you, Mr. Policeman."

And the policeman said, "Don't mention it," and turned to go down the stairs again.

"Just a moment, Policeman," said Mr. Snooks. "You mustn't go down the stairs in the dark. You might fall." And taking a box of matches, he LIT THE CANDLE AGAIN!

Mr. Snooks went down the stairs with the policeman and saw him out of the door. His footsteps went blump, blump, blump along the quiet street.

John Snooks and little Ann Snooks went back to bed. Mr. and Mrs. Snooks got into bed again. There was silence for a moment.

"Mr. Snooks," said Mrs. Snooks, "would you blow out the candle?"

Mr. Snook got out of bed. "Certainly, Mrs. Snooks," he said . . .

And so on AD INFINITUM.

—*Harcourt Williams*

52

The Shopping Trip

The leader tells the story and accompanies it with motions. The audience mimics the motions. Each motion, once started, is continued after the next one begins so that before the end of the story, hands, feet, head and jaws are all in motion.

We're all going on a shopping trip in the big department store.
   (*Name a local one.*)

We're going to buy a pair of scissors first.
   (*Cutting motion with forefinger and middle finger of right hand.*)

We need a new set of steps for the back porch.

(Walking-up-steps motion with feet.)

There was a sale of rocking chairs so we bought one.

(Rocking motion back and forth in chair while walking with feet and cutting with fingers.)

We got thirsty walking around and put a big piece of bubble gum in our mouths.

(Make lump in cheek with tongue and begin chewing.)

At this moment our heads began to itch.

(Scratch heads and remember to continue all motions.)

The salesman came up to us and asked if we wanted to buy anything else and we all said, "No."

(Shake head from side to side and continue all motions.)

I Went to the Library

Storytellers often make up their own special games for the stretch period. In this one, each player in turn has his chance to name a book title, but he must repeat all the previously named titles to stay in the game. Those who cannot remember all previous titles are out; the last player wins the game. If the group is too large, a few at a time may be chosen to play.

LEADER: I went to the library and I read *Tom Sawyer*. (*Any title may be chosen.*)

FIRST PLAYER: I went to the library and I read *Tom Sawyer* and *Curious George*. (*Another title is added.*)

SECOND PLAYER: I went to the library and I read *Tom Sawyer* and *Curious George* and *Homer Price*. (*A third title is added.*)

THIRD PLAYER: I went to the library and I read *Tom Sawyer* and *Curious George* and *Homer Price* and *Treasure Island*. (*Four titles.*)

Game continues until each child has had a turn and goes on until only one child is left as winner.

FINGER PLAYS

Some of these finger plays are very well known. You may know others also, or you may want to make up your own.

Clap Your Hands

Carry out actions indicated by the rhyme. Other actions may be added at the suggestion of the children, such as "wiggle your ears," "touch your nose," or "make a fist."

Clap your hands, clap your hands,
Clap them just like me.

Touch your shoulders, touch your shoulders,
Touch them just like me.

Tap your knees, tap your knees,
Tap them just like me.

Shake your head, shake your head,
Shake them just like me.

Clap your hands, clap your hands,
Now let them quiet be.

Who Feels Happy?

Who feels happy? Who feels gay?
All who do, clap their hands this way.
 (Clap hands.)

Who feels happy? Who feels gay?
All who do, nod their heads this way.
 (Nod head.)

Who feels happy? Who feels gay?
All who do, tap their shoulders this way.
 (Tap shoulder with hand.)

Further actions may be suggested by the children. "Tap your feet," "swing your arms," and other motions can be added.

Hands Up

Carry out actions indicated by the rhyme.

Reach for the ceiling
Touch the floor,
Stand up again,
Let's do more.
Touch your head,
Then your knee;
Up to your shoulder,
Like this, see.
Reach for the ceiling
Touch the floor.
That's all now—
There isn't anymore.

My Eyes Can See

My eyes can see.
    (Make "eyeglasses" with hands.)
My mouth can talk.
    (Move thumb and index finger as if talking.)
My ears can hear.
    (Cup hand and place it behind ear.)
My feet can walk.
    (Make second and third fingers of right hand "walk.")
My nose can smell.
    (Touch nose.)
My teeth can bite.
    (Move fingers together and apart as if chewing.)
My lids can flutter.
    (Hold hands up to eyes and flutter fingers.)
My hands can write.
    (Pretend to hold pen and write.)
But when the clock
Its time doth show,
I'll take some books
    (Pick up some books.)
And away I'll go.
    (Wave good-bye.)

The Teapot

I'm a little teapot, short and stout.
This is my handle,
> *(Put one hand on hip.)*
This is my spout.
> *(Extend opposite hand outward and slant it down for spout.)*
When I get all steamed up and shout,
Just tip me over and pour me out.
> *(Bend body toward arm extended as spout.)*

The Turtle

There was a little turtle.
He lived in a box.
(Put index finger of right hand in upward palm of left hand.)
He swam in a puddle.
(Make circular motion as if in a puddle.)
He climbed on the rocks.
(Climb over the fingertips for "rocks.")

He snapped at a mosquito;
(Make snapping motion by raising and lowering fingers and thumb of right hand.)
He snapped at a flea;
He snapped at a minnow;
He snapped at me.

He caught the mosquito.
(Clasp and unclasp as if catching something.)
He caught the flea;
He caught the minnow;
But he didn't catch me.
(Point to self.)

Eensy Weensy Spider

The eensy, weensy spider
    (Extend and curve right-hand fingers.)
Climbed up the waterspout.
    (Fingers climb, spider-fashion up the left arm.)
Down came the rain
    (Sweep hands down and open wide.)
And washed the spider out.
Out came the sun
    (Make big circle with arms over head.)
And dried up all the rain.
So eensy, weensy spider
    (Make spider with curved fingers.)
Climbed up the spout again.
    (Fingers of right hand climb up the left arm again.)

RIDDLES

Some of the riddles here are like puzzles; you must guess the answers. Other riddles have trick endings. You may have your own favorites which you will want to share with the rest of your group.

Transportation Problem

Once there was a man who was set the task of taking a wolf, a goat, and a cabbage across the river. When he came to the river, he found that the boat was so small it would hold one man and only ONE OTHER thing.

What was he to do? How could he take the wolf, the goat, and the cabbage over, one at a time, so that the wolf wouldn't eat the goat and the goat wouldn't eat the cabbage?

ANSWERS:

4. Go back and get the goat.
3. Take the wolf over (leaving the goat behind).
2. Take the cabbage over and take the goat back.
1. Take the goat over.

OR

4. Go back and get the goat.
3. Take the cabbage over (leaving the goat behind).
2. Take the wolf over and take the goat back.
1. Take the goat over.

Endless Riddles

LEADER: Pete and Repeat were walking down the
street. Suddenly Pete went away.
Who was left?

GROUP: Repeat.

LEADER: Pete and Repeat were walking down the
street. Suddenly Pete went away.
Who was left? (*in louder voice*)

GROUP: Repeat.

LEADER: PETE AND REPEAT WERE WALKING, etc.
(*very loud*)

Continue to repeat the riddle louder and louder and more impatiently until the group dissolves in laughter.

LEADER: 'E was the greatest man on earth.

GROUP: Who was?

LEADER: 'E was.

GROUP: Who was 'e?

LEADER: 'Arry 'Arrington.

GROUP: Who was 'Arry 'Arrington?

LEADER: 'E was the greatest man on earth.

GROUP: Who was?

Leader continues to repeat the riddle until group stops repeating the response of its own accord.

American Riddles

1. Fiery little captain
   Of early Pilgrim fame;
   Close friend of John Alden—
   Can you tell his name?

2. Two cousins who had the same last name
   Were very unlike, yet both won fame.
   Rough Rider was one, then President.
   The other, twelve years in the White House spent.

3. She who came to us from France
   Holds a torch high in her hand;
   Welcomes travelers from afar,
   Coming to our friendly land.

4. Known by a nickname, this scout of the West
   Chased hostile Indians, rode by Pony Express.

5. Like a famous President
   Was this great man's name;
   And the lowly peanut
   Helped to bring him fame.

6. What bus crossed the ocean?

7. What has 18 legs and catches flies?

8. Why does the Statue of Liberty stand in New York Harbor?

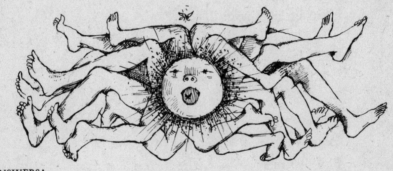

ANSWERS:

8. Because it cannot sit down.
7. A baseball team.
6. Columbus.
5. George Washington Carver.
4. Buffalo Bill.
3. Statue of Liberty.
2. Theodore Roosevelt; Franklin Roosevelt.
1. Captain Miles Standish.

More Riddles

Once there was a donkey in a field and on one side of the field stood a ten-foot wall. On the other side a wide deep river flowed, and along the third side ran a thick prickly hedge. On the fourth side a steep high cliff rose. In a field close by there was a heap of carrots. How did the donkey get to the carrots?

Most groups supply the following answers:

GROUP: Jump over the wall?

LEADER: No, it was too high.

GROUP: Swim the river?

LEADER: No, he couldn't swim.

GROUP: Push through the hedge?

LEADER: No, it was too thick and prickly.

GROUP: Climb the cliff?

LEADER: No, it was too steep.

GROUP *(correct answer)*: Well, we don't know.

LEADER: Neither did the donkey.

67

1. What would happen very soon
   If you swallowed your cereal spoon?

2. Riddle me, riddle me, riddle me reet,
   When do elephants have eight feet?

3. What can you see
      Down in the lake?
   That's always free
      But that no one can take?

4. What do the children
      In China call
   Young yellow cats
      When they are small?

ANSWERS:

4. Kittens.
3. The moon.
2. When there are two elephants.
1. You couldn't stir your cereal.

SONGS

Here are some songs which you will enjoy singing and acting out. For more fun, you can make up your own words and actions for many of them.

Smoke Goes up the Chimney

This song may be sung on one note or made-up tune.

Oh, you push the damper in (*push right arm forward*)
And you pull the damper out (*pull arm back*)
And the smoke goes up the chimney (*make spiral motion*)
Just the same. Just the same (*wave right arm to side; wave left arm
    to side*)
And the smoke goes up the chimney just the same.

Sing song with all the motions.
*Repeat and be quiet on "push damper in" but make motion in
    rhythm.*
*Repeat and be quiet on "push damper in" and "pull the damper
    out" but make motions in rhythm.*
*Repeat and be quiet on "push damper in" and "pull the damper
    out" and the first "smoke goes up the chimney" but make
    motions in rhythm.*
Repeat and be quiet on all lines. Make motions.
The last time you sing, the only words will be:

    Oh, you (*motion*)
    And you (*motion*)
    And the (*motion*) (*motion*) (*motion*)
    And the (*motion*)

If You're Happy and You Know It

If you're happy and you know it, clap your hands,
  (*Clap clap*)
If you're happy and you know it, clap your hands,
  (*Clap clap*)
If you're happy and you know it, then the whole wide world will
  know it,
If you're happy and you know it, clap your hands.
  (*Clap, clap*)

Other verses may include all kinds of actions, such as:

stamp your feet	wiggle your ears
touch your toes	cross your legs

Today Is Monday

Today is Monday, today is Monday
Monday, string beans
All you hungry children
Come and eat it up.

Today is Tuesday, today is Tuesday
Tuesday, spaghetti
Monday, string beans
All you hungry children
Come and eat it up.

Today is Wednesday, today is Wednesday
Wednesday, zooooop
Tuesday, spaghetti
Monday, string beans
All you hungry children
Come and eat it up.

Today is Thursday, today is Thursday
Thursday, roast beef . . .
(*continue as in third verse*)

Today is Friday, today is Friday
Friday, fresh fish . . .
(*continue as in fourth verse*)

Today is Saturday, today is Saturday
Saturday, chicken . . .
(*continue as in fifth verse*)

Today is Sunday . . .
Sunday, ice cream . . .
(*continue as in sixth verse*)

You may wish to make up your own menu after the first time.

Bingo

FIRST TIME: *The leader sings song straight through.*

SECOND TIME: *The whole group repeats song but keeps silent on letter* B; *clap hands in rhythm instead of singing* B.

THIRD TIME: *Repeat song but keep silent on letters* B *and* I; *clap hands in rhythm instead of singing* B *and* I.

FOURTH TIME: *Repeat song but keep silent on letters* B *and* I *and* N; *clap hands in rhythm instead of singing* B, I, N.

Continue to repeat song, keeping silent on each successive letter. Final and sixth time will have five claps instead of singing BINGO.

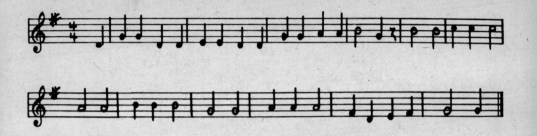

There was a farmer had a dog;
And Bingo was his name, sir.
B I N G O, B I N G O
B I N G O
Bingo was his name, sir.

That farmer's dog at our back door;
Begging for a bone, sir.
B I N G O, B I N G O
B I N G O
Bingo was his name, sir.

I Wish I Was a Mole in the Ground

I wish I was a mole in the ground,
I wish I was a mole in the ground,
If I was a mole in the ground,
I'd root that mountain down,
And I wish I was a mole in the ground.

I wish I was a lizard in the spring,
I wish I was a lizard in the spring,
If I was a lizard in the spring,
I'd hear my sweetheart sing,
And I wish I was a lizard in the spring.

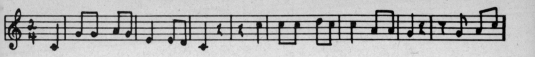

*Sing the song through once or twice. Then ask individual children
to make wishes. Make up a rhyme on the spur of the moment and
continue the song. The following are some examples made up by
children in a library story hour.*

I wish I was a horse in the stable,
I wish I was a horse in the stable,
If I was a horse in the stable,
I'd canter when I was able,
I wish I was a horse in the stable.

I wish I was an ant in the grass,
I wish I was an ant in the grass,
If I was an ant in the grass,
I'd tickle a little lass,
I wish I was an ant in the grass.

I wish I was a bird in a tree,
I wish I was a bird in a tree,
If I was a bird in a tree,
I'd see what I could see,
I wish I was a bird in a tree.

My Bonnie Lies over the Ocean

My bonnie lies over the ocean,
My bonnie lies over the sea,
My bonnie lies over the ocean,
Oh, bring back my bonnie to me.

Bring back, bring back,
Oh, bring back my bonnie to me . . . to me.
Bring back, bring back,
Oh, bring back my bonnie to me.

1. *Sing the whole song through the first time with no motions.*
2. *Repeat the whole song a second time with the following motions for each word:*

> *"my"—point to self*
> *"bonnie"—make figure of a girl in the air with*
>   *both hands*

"lies"—put hands together and make a circle with
    the arms to indicate a cradle or bed

"over"—point to faraway with hand motion

"ocean"—make ocean waves in wavy motion of the
    right hand

"sea"—make wavy motion with right hand, but
    with a choppy, sharper stroke to differenti-
    ate from "ocean."

"oh"—join thumbs and index fingers in round O

"bring"—make beckoning motion with right hand

"back"—touch back of left shoulder with right
    hand

"to"—hold up two fingers

"me"—point again to self

3. Go through the motions slowly with the group once or twice;
then try whole song.

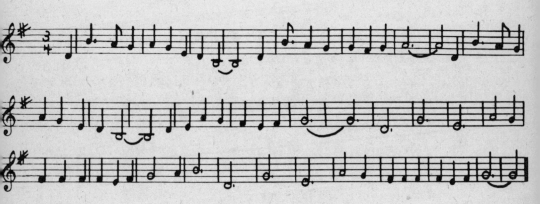

79

John Brown's Baby

John Brown's baby had a cold upon his chest,
John Brown's baby had a cold upon his chest,
John Brown's baby had a cold upon his chest,
And they rubbed him down with camphorated oil.

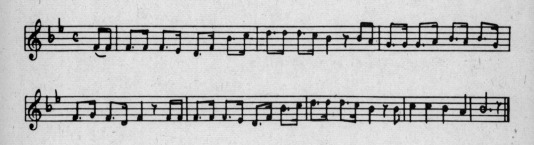

1. *Sing the whole song through the first time with no motions.*
2. *Repeat whole song a second time, but remain silent on the word "baby." Instead, join arms together to make a circle in the shape of a cradle with a baby in it. Rock cradle each time word "baby" occurs.*
3. *Repeat song a third time; remain silent on words "baby" and "cold." Make cradling motion on word "baby" and make a loud coughing sound in place of the word "cold."*

4. Repeat song a fourth time; remain silent on words "baby," "cold," and "chest." Substitute cradling motion for "baby"; substitute a loud cough for "cold"; substitute a tap on the chest with the right hand for the word "chest."

5. Repeat the whole song a fifth time; remain silent on words "baby," "cold," "chest," "rubbed." Substitute cradling motion for "baby"; substitute a cough for "cold"; substitute a tap on the chest for "chest"; substitute a rubbing motion on the stomach for "rubbed."

Mister Rabbit

Mister Rabbit, Mister Rabbit, your ears mighty long,
  (*Hold hands on top of head to make ears*)
Yes, my Lawd, they're put on wrong.
  (*Nod head in agreement*)

REFRAIN
Every little soul must shine, shine, shine,
  (*Wind fists away from the body in slow circular motion*)
Every little soul must shine, shine, shine.
  (*Wind fists in* FAST *circular motion toward yourself*)

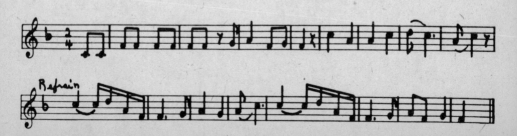

Mister Rabbit, Mister Rabbit, your coat mighty gray,
   (*Pat arm as though patting coat of animal*)
Yes, my Lawd, 'twas made that way.
   (*Nod head in agreement*)

Every little soul must shine, shine, shine,
   (*Wind fists away from the body in low circular motion*)
Every little soul must shine, shine, shine.
   (*Wind fists in* FAST *circular motion toward yourself*)

Mister Rabbit, Mister Rabbit, your feet mighty red,
   (*Point to feet; wiggle feet*)
Yes, my Lawd, I'm almost dead.
   (*Close eyes, let body go limp as if dead, fold hands in prayer
   position*)

REFRAIN: *same as above*

Mister Rabbit, Mister Rabbit, your tail mighty white,
   (*Make hand motions to indicate long tail*)
Yes, my Lawd, and I'm a-getting out of sight.
   (*Close eyes with both palms of hands*)

REFRAIN: *same as above*

One Finger Keep Moving

1. One finger keep moving,
     (Hold up right index finger and begin wiggling it)
   One finger keep moving,
     (Wiggle finger again and stop)
   One finger keep moving,
     (Start finger wiggling)
   And we'll all be happy and gay.
     (Continue wiggling finger)

2. One finger
     (Hold up right index finger)
   Two fingers,
     (Hold up left index finger)
   Keep moving.
     (Wiggle both index fingers)
   One finger,
     (Stop wiggling fingers; hold up right index finger)
   Two fingers,
     (Show left index finger)
   Keep moving.
     (Wiggle both fingers while singing)
   One finger, two fingers keep moving,
     (Show right, then left forefingers and keep both wiggling)
   And we'll all be happy and gay.
     (Wiggle both fingers)

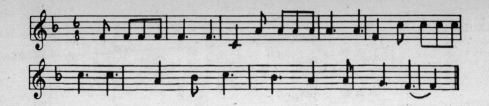

3. One finger, two fingers, one thumb, two thumbs keep moving, etc.

   (Continue the song by showing each part of the body mentioned and adding one portion at a time as the words dictate; during the singing of "And we'll all be happy and gay," all the accumulated motions must be kept going.)

4. One finger, two fingers, one thumb, two thumbs, one arm, two arms keep moving, etc.

5. One finger, two fingers, one thumb, two thumbs, one arm, two arms, one foot, two feet, etc.

6. One finger, two fingers, one thumb, two thumbs, one arm, two arms, one foot, two feet, one head (nod head up and down), keep moving, etc.

7. One finger, two fingers, one thumb, two thumbs, one arm, two arms, one foot, two feet, one head, stand up, sit down, keep moving, etc.

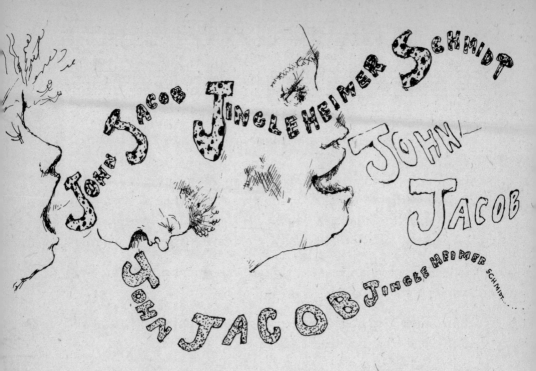

John Jacob Jingleheimer Schmidt

Repeat this song as many times as you wish, each time more and more softly. Finally, the words are repeated silently until the last line, which is shouted as loudly as possible.

John Jacob Jingleheimer Schmidt!
His name is my name too;
Whenever we go out,
Hear the happy people shout;
John Jacob Jingleheimer Schmidt!
Ta ra ra ra ra ra ra

John Jacob Jingleheimer Schmidt!
His name is my name too;
Whenever we go out,
Hear the happy people shout;
John Jacob Jingleheimer Schmidt!
Ta ra ra ra ra ra ra

John Jacob Jingleheimer Schmidt!
His name is my name too;
Whenever we go out,
Hear the happy people shout;
John Jacob Jingleheimer Schmidt!
Ta ra ra ra ra ra ra

Put Your Finger in the Air

Act out motions as verses suggest.

Put your finger in the air, in the air,
Put your finger in the air, in the air,
Put your finger in the air. Tell me, how's the air up there?
Put your finger in the air, in the air.

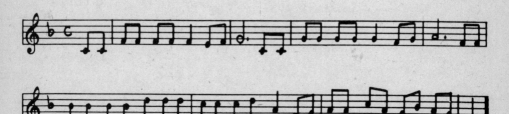

Words & Music by Woody Guthrie.
TRO — © Copyright 1954 Folkways Music Publishers, Inc.,
New York, New York. Used by permission.

Put your finger on your head, on your head,
    (Repeat)
Put your finger on your head. Tell me, is it green or red?
    (Repeat first line)

Put your finger on your cheek, on your cheek,
    (Repeat)
Put your finger on your cheek. Leave it there a week.
    (Repeat first line)

Put your finger on your nose, on your nose,
    (Repeat)
Put your finger on your nose. Is that where the cold wind blows?
    (Repeat first line)

Put your finger on your chest, on your chest,
    (Repeat)
Put your finger on your chest. Give it just a little rest.
    (Repeat first line)

Put your finger on your belly, on your belly,
    (Repeat)
Put your finger on your belly. Make it shake like apply jelly.
    (Repeat first line)

—*Woody Guthrie*

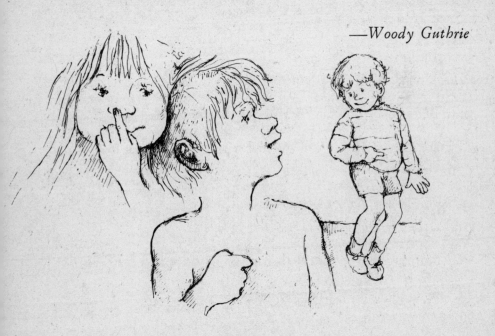

TONGUE TWISTERS AND JOKES

Many children have enjoyed the tongue twisters and nonsense jokes included here. You will have other favorites to share with your group.

SAY QUICKLY:

A schmoo slyly slowly shuffled a snorkle full of slush.

Billy Botter baked biscuits with bitter butter in the batter.

The rat ran over the ridge of the roof with a raw lump of liver in his mouth.

A big black bug bit a big black bear,
And made the big black bear bleed blood.

Sally Simpson sold the seashells Sandy saw sitting on the seashore.

Six long slim slick sycamore saplings.

NICE OLD LADY: And what are *you* going to do, Billy, when you get as big as your father?

BILLY: Go on a diet.

BOASTFUL BOB: My father is an Elk, a Lion and a Moose.

PRACTICAL PETE: So how much does it cost to see him?

BOB: What a terrible bump on your head! What did that?

SAM: Tomatoes.

BOB: Heavens! How could tomatoes cause a huge bump like that?

SAM: They were in a can!

TEACHER: What is a cannibal?

BOB: I don't know.

TEACHER: Well, what would you be if you ate your mother and father?

BOB: An orphan.

TEACHER: Tommy, your hands are very dirty. What would you say if I came to school with dirty hands?

TOMMY: I'd be too polite to mention it.

BILL: What can a five-ton elephant do?

JOE: A-N-Y-T-H-I-N-G he wants!

Acknowledgments

Grateful acknowledgment is made to the following publishers and individuals, for permission to reprint copyrighted material in this book:

Abelard-Schuman Limited for five riddles from RIDDLES, RIDDLES EVERYWHERE by Ennis Rees, copyright 1964 by Ennis Rees; and for two tongue twisters from RAINBOW IN THE MORNING by Carl Withers and Alta Jablow, copyright 1956 by Carl Withers and Alta Jablow. All rights reserved.

Abingdon Press for "Smoke Goes up the Chimney" from ACT IT OUT by Bernice Wells Carlson, copyright 1956 by Pierce and Washabaugh; and for eight American History riddles from AMERICAN RIDDLES IN RHYME by Ruby B. Murphy, copyright 1955 by Pierce and Washabaugh. The Bodley Head Limited for "The Snooks Family" from TALES FROM EBONY by Harcourt Williams.

Mrs. Margaret G. Burroughs for "Head and Shoulders, Baby" and "Who Did?" from DID YOU FEED MY COW? published by Thomas Y. Crowell Company in 1956.

The Clarendon Press, Oxford, for the basic story of "The Dark House" and for the riddle of the donkey from THE LORE AND LANGUAGE OF SCHOOLCHILDREN by Iona and Peter Opie, 1959.

William Cole for "If You Ever" from I WENT TO THE ANIMAL FARM.

Collins & World Publishing Company for "The Rat Ran Over the Ridge of the Roof" from MORE TONGUE TANGLERS AND A RIGMAROLE by Charles Francis Potter, copyright © 1964 by Clara Cook Potter and "Transportation Problem" from NOODLES, NITWITS & NUMSKULLS by Maria Leach, copyright © 1961 by Maria Leach.

Thomas Y. Crowell Company, New York, for five limericks from LAUGHABLE LIMERICKS by Sara and John E. Brewton, text copyright © 1965 by Sara and John E. Brewton.

Doubleday & Company, Inc. for five jokes from THE REAL BOOK OF JOKES by Margaret Gossett, copyright 1954 by Frank Folsom and Mary Elting Folsom.

Harcourt Brace Jovanovich, Inc., for "What Did You Put in Your Pocket?" from SOMETHING SPECIAL by Beatrice Schenk de Regniers, text © 1958 by Beatrice Schenk de Regniers.

Harper & Row, Publishers, Inc, for "The Busy Farmer's Wife," "The Shopping Trip," "The Lion Hunt," and "One Finger Keep Moving" from FUN AND GAMES by Margaret E. Mulac, copyright © 1956 by Harper & Row, Publishers, Inc.

Hart Publishing Company, Inc., for three riddles from BEST RIDDLES by Jeff Thompson.

Harvard University Press for the accompaniment to the song "Mister Rabbit" from ON THE

INDEX OF TITLES